GRANNIES DON'T FART

BONNEY
PRESS

Lisa Regan • Agnès Ernoult

Published by Bonney Press
an imprint of Hinkler Pty Ltd
45–55 Fairchild Street
Heatherton Victoria 3202 Australia
www.hinkler.com

BONNEY
PRESS

© Hinkler Pty Ltd 2020

Author: Lisa Regan
Illustrator: Agnès Ernoult
Editorial: Zoe Antony
Art Direction: Paul Scott

ISBN: 978 1 4889 1882 7

Printed and bound in China

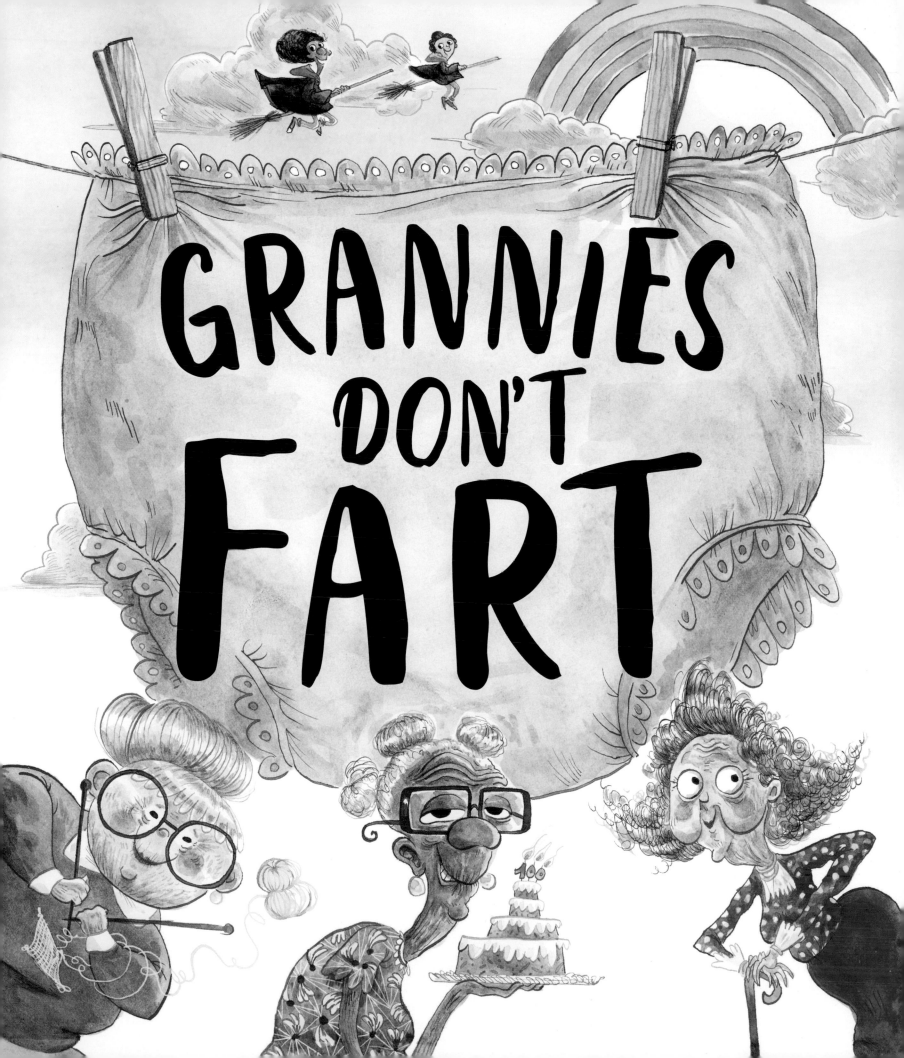

Fizz and all his wizard friends are playing his new game.

Since they proved their mums DO fart, life had been quite tame.

Fizz is moaning to his mum,

'Gran's party will be BORING.
Full of all her ancient friends — all tedious...
or snoring!'

Mum slams shut her magic book. She splutters with frustration.

'It's Mabel's hundredth birthday! It's a cause for celebration.'

She rises up and waves her wand.
'Take these invitations.
Deliver them to Granny's friends
and all of our relations.'

Fizz calls the crew for back-up – he can't do this on his own.
The old farts need their letters, so they set off... with a groan.

Then something yucky dawns on Sam.
The blood drains from his face:

'DO GRANNIES guff? I think we have
our next detective case!'

They hurry off to find Sam's nan: the first name on the list.

She's in the pool for Aquafit. The boys just can't resist.

'Let's watch a while for research. We won't cause any trouble.'

Sam groans out loud as Nanny Joan lets rip a mighty bubble.

The gang decide to find out more, to seek illumination.

They call on Ethan's grandma in her shared accommodation.

Bouquet Home
FOR RETIRED
WITCHES &
WIZARDS

Their noses curl as they approach. Blimey, what's that stink?
A whiff of cabbage in the air — enough to make them blink.

Grandma Ivy claps her hands. 'A **party? How delightful!** I'd love to come. Will there be cake? The food in here is frightful.'

The farting question must be asked. They gently quiz her first.

'**Ooh, better out than in, my boy! If you don't parp, you'll burst!**'

Marty's shocked. He finds his gran, and wakes her from her snooze.

'Can you help me with this crossword? Listen to these clues...'

'7 down begins with T. A card that helps you win.'

She makes a sudden bottom noise.
'TRUMP!' shouts Ethan with a grin.

Harriet laughs and gives a wink.
'You should hear Mighty Mabel.
Her parps are quite the loudest here - the tea
flies off the table!'

honk!

The oldies all join the fun. The fart talk makes them titter.

'We've formed a gang called hashtag guffs. We're trending now on Twitter!'

#GUFFS

toot!

'In the past,' says Granny Rose, 'it just wasn't allowed for ladies to pass wind at all; though men did, loud and proud.'

'So now we have decided that enough must be enough.
We're all past caring, anyhow. So what if grannies guff?!'

The boys decide to get some air, so walk into the garden.
Feeding strays is Mrs Botts. Whoops! She begs her pardon.

They laugh so much it makes things worse. She gives another wiggle.

'Life's too short to be uptight,' she points out with a giggle.

The boys head back to Fizz's mum to tell her what they've found.

'Really, boys, this is absurd.
You must stop fooling 'round.'

Happy 100th Mabel!

'You might find farting funny now,
but once you're more mature,
you'll see that toilet humour
is just fun for kids, I'm sure.'

Fizz is flabbergasted, while Ethan rolls his eyes.
They think their prudish mothers might be in for a surprise!

The guests arrive, the party starts and laughter fills the room.

They've all pitched in to buy a gift: a brand new scooter broom!

Outside there's a tournament they never thought they'd see.
It's Mabel versus Ivy in the pensioner Grand Prix!

And then
it's time for
birthday cake.

'Now, on the count of three...'

They all blow hard.

Oops! What a stench! Mabel smiles with glee.

fwarp!

Fizz's mum is outraged. 'Oh, mother! How uncouth! I expect your generation to be a model for our youth!'

'Ah, who cares? It's just a fart! There's no need to get mad!

At a century old, I've changed my mind about what is good and bad.'